The Toddlers' Coloring Book

The
New Testament
Stories

VICTOR BOOKS
A DIVISION OF SCRIPTURE PRESS PUBLICATIONS INC.
USA CANADA ENGLAND

An Angel Brings Good News

"You will have a special baby," an angel says.

"He will be Baby Jesus." Mary is so happy.

Baby Jesus

**Baby Jesus is sleeping.
Shhh.**

**The animals see Baby Jesus.
Do you think they are quiet too?**

Shepherds Visit Jesus

**"Good News," angels say. "Baby Jesus is born."
The shepherds are so happy.**

**The shepherds go to Bethlehem.
They want to see this special baby.**

Wise Men Visit Jesus

**Wise men give wonderful gifts to Baby Jesus.
Would you like to give Him something too?**

The Boy Jesus

The Boy Jesus helps Joseph.
He makes things from wood.

Jesus in the Temple

Jesus is growing up.
He is teaching the teachers about God

Mary and Joseph take care of Jesus.
And God takes care of Mary and Joseph.

John Baptizes Jesus

**John is God's helper.
He baptized Jesus. Jesus told him to.**

**"Jesus is My Son," God says.
"He pleases Me."**

Jesus Goes Fishing

"Put your nets over there," Jesus says.

**Jesus' friends obey Him.
Now look at all those fish.**

Down through the Roof

**"Heal our friend," some men ask Jesus.
But they cannot get near Jesus.**

**They let the man down
through a hole in the roof.
Jesus can heal him now.**

Jesus Chooses Twelve Helpers

"I want twelve helpers," Jesus says.

**"Thank You," say the twelve helpers.
"We're happy we can help You."**

Jesus Stops a Storm

**Look at that storm.
Do you see Jesus' boat bouncing up and down?**

**"Stop storm!" Jesus says.
The storm obeys Jesus. Do you?**

Lunch for 5,000

The people are glad they can be with Jesus.

**"May I have your lunch?" Jesus asks a boy.
Jesus will feed 5,000 people with it.**

Jesus Walks on Water

**Jesus' friends are in trouble.
Their boat is about to sink.**

**But here comes Jesus.
He is walking on the water.
Jesus will help His friends.**

Lazarus Is Alive!

**Lazarus has died. But Jesus talks to him.
Now he is alive.**

Only God's Son can make a dead person live again.

Jesus Loves Children

These children want to talk with Jesus.

"Come to Me," says Jesus.
Do you like to talk with Jesus too?

Zacchaeus

**Zacchaeus wants to see Jesus.
But Zacchaeus is too short.**

**Zacchaeus climbs a tree. He sees Jesus!
Now Zacchaeus is happy.**

Jesus Rides into Jerusalem

Jesus is riding into Jerusalem.

That's why these people are so happy.

The Last Supper

Jesus is eating with His friends.

**"Remember Me," Jesus says.
Do you think they will?**

Jesus Prays in a Garden

Jesus' friends wait while He prays.

**"Help Me do what You want," Jesus prays.
That's good for us to pray too.**

Jesus Dies on the Cross

Jesus is dying to take away our sin.

Will you ask Him to be your Saviour?

Some Women Visit Jesus' Tomb

**"Jesus has risen," the angel says.
That's Good News, isn't it?**

Mary runs to tell the others that Jesus is alive.

Jesus Goes Back to Heaven

**Look! Jesus is going up into heaven.
"He will come back," an angel says.**

Saul Becomes Jesus' Friend

**Saul hated Jesus and His friends.
But one day Jesus talked to Saul from heaven.
Now Saul loves Jesus.
He will help Jesus do His work.**

Singing in Jail

Paul and Silas are in jail.
Some bad men put them there.

**Paul and Silas are singing about Jesus.
Now the man in charge wants
to follow Jesus, too.**

A Boy Named Timothy

**Timothy's mother and grandmother
help him love Jesus.**

**Does someone help you love
Jesus and God's Word?**

Jesus is happy when you love Him.